Posy Simmonds
VERY POSY

Fontana/Collins

To my mother

First published by Jonathan Cape 1985
First issued in Fontana Paperbacks 1987

Copyright © Posy Simmonds 1985

Made and printed in Great Britain by
William Collins Sons & Co. Ltd, Glasgow

The drawings in this book have been taken from episodes of
The Silent Three, a weekly cartoon strip appearing in the
Guardian, and from *Harper's Magazine*, New York.

Village Christmas

December 22

December 23

December 24

December 25

December 26

December 27

© P. Simmonds

© Posy Simmonds 1983

The Weber family have just seen the *happiest, all-star family show* in town!

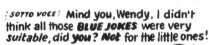

© Posy Simmonds

© Posy Simmonds 1984

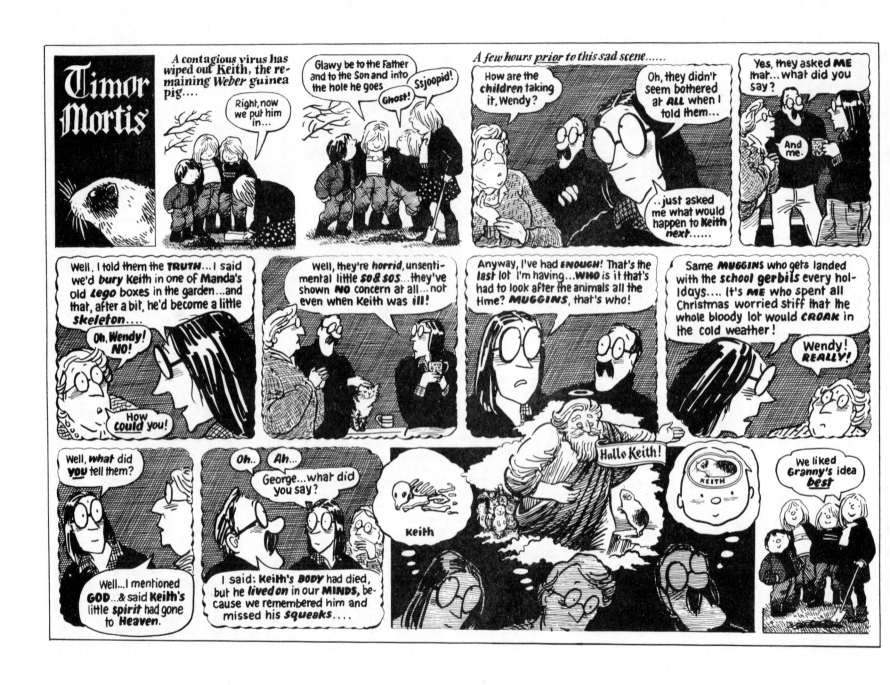

MOMMA'S FAULT!

Wendy Weber likes to keep part of the day to *herself*.... *...a private* time, when she can loose the reins of *domesticity* and continue working on her thesis......

...or, sometimes, if the Muse fails:

Magnolia Place Part 2

Oh Momma! I don't *care!* I'm gonna *keep* this **BABY**...and I'm gonna do it **RIGHT**! I'm gonna be a *real* mother!

GASP: Why, Donna!

I'm gonna be a *mother* who's **ALWAYS** *there*...to share **EVERY** joy...to wipe away **EVERY** tear!

GASP: Oh Honey!

NOT like **YOU**, Momma! CHOKE! Where **WERE YOU** all my life?

You were **ALWAYS** someplace else.... ...**ALWAYS** your *bureau* came **FIRST!**

All my life, I **NEVER** came home to the *smell* of **BAKING** SOB!

Oh Donna! SOB!

I tried...

...**Gaad** knows I tried!

I wanted you to feel **FREE**, Donna! ..to lead your own life! ..I didn't want to **PRY**, to **FUSS**...to **SMOTHER!**

UNLIKE you, Mother! You *smothered* **ME!**

GASP: Why... Susan!

GASP: Why... Momma!

You **NEVER** let me **ALONE!** You couldn't **CUT** the **CORD!** SOB! You **FUSSED!** You **STUFFED** me full of home made **COOKIES!**

Oh Susan!

I tried... Dear **Gaad**, I tried!

I wanted you to have all the things I never had... *love...security*.. I wanted to be *there*...to share *every* joy...to wipe away *every* tear...

NOT like **YOU**, Mama! **Where** were **YOU** all my life?!

GASP: Why Mother!

Why Grandmother!

GASP: Why... Hannah!

You left me to the *servants*... I only saw you **10 minutes** a day in the drawing room!

Oh Hannah! I *tried*... Lord knows I *tried*... ...I didn't want to spoil you...I didn't want to *smother* you....

Not like **YOU**, Mother! You *smothered* me ever since I was a little bitty girl...

GASP: O Grand-Mother!

O Great-Grandmother!

O Mother!

GASP: Why.. Louella!

Read to us!

We been waiting and waiting!

Come on! Mummee!

Mummee... Why don't you come!

Come & wipe me

Come and tuck us up!

© Posy Simmonds

In his GOOD Books

Dining with one's husband's colleagues is one of the favours an academic's wife feels bound to bestow.....

Oh *God*, George! Do I *have* to ?!

Diary 1982

....but this is a *bit* MUCH: having to help butter up a visiting member of the Board of External Assessors, on whose *fateful* report the standing of the faculty depends.....

I *know* he's a pretentious old bore, Wendy! But we *have* to go... Anita's pulling out all the culinary stops....

Awfully GOOD of you all to entertain me so *royally*, Gavin...

well... nice to see you.

Oh, don't mention...

.. er.. you mentioned the reading list for the vacation...

Yes, there *ARE* some books one returns to again and again aren't there? One sort of *recuperates* with them, doesn't one..?

Absolutely!

Yes, like touching *BASE*...

I mean... over the summer... I always re-read the whole of *Bachelard*... he *completely* recharges the batteries!

Ah, really?

Yes, he's not *un*interesting, is he?

Ah, yes... Bachelard!

That's *not* what George usually says about *Bachelard*

... and *Hölderlin*... his *oeuvre is* very precious to me!

Ah yes... *Hölderlin*...

Mmm

I always read *Goethe's Letters*... Chronologically backwards – it's an infallible *rejuvenator*....

Goethe!? Oh *no!*

I think the *whole* of pre-*Wilhelmine* Germany is *too* culturally *normative*... its resonance is so *UTTERLY* self-reflexive!

! Ah..

er.. yes it is a bit.

What about *Butor*? And *Robbe-Grillet*?

Oh NO! Come! Surely *NOT*?

They're *SO* aggressively *ROMANTIC*!

... and the association of the *Nouvelle Vague chez eux*.... so unfocused!

Ah.. well... you may have a point there...

Ah

Quite!

They're just *sucking up*!

And what about *you*? Do *you* have a *literary life-raft*?

Who? *Me*? Um well... Yes...

"The Tale of Mrs Tiggy-Winkle"... ... I can read that over and over...

Oh, *Potter*! She *is* extra-ordinarily interesting, isn't she?

I mean, some people might prefer her darker allegories... Mr Todd... Samuel Whiskers... or *Squirrel Nutkin* as a study of *external menace*... paranoia....

Oh.. yes she...

Ah, yes, *Potter*...

Yes.. I mean, take *Puddle-Duck's* location within the *Potter*-text...

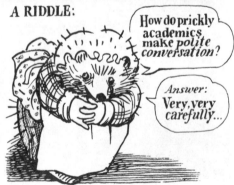

A RIDDLE:

How do prickly academics make *polite* conversation?

Answer: Very, very carefully...

A SOAP OPERA

Act 1 takes place in a richly appointed home, where *Trish*, a wife & mother, is swearing piteously at the tumble drier, which has again betrayed her...

She bemoans her lot as Drudge ...& a husband who considers her tasks trivial.

****! Oh!

Enter *Stanhope*, her spouse, a middle-aged burgher. He berates her: what has *she* to bewail? Does *he* not toil a 30 hour week, whilst she has:-

A ve·ry ea·sy number And a very cushy life... Enjoying all the perks Of a Stay·at·home Wife!

O Dio!

Heartsick, *Trish* tells him just *where* he can shove the rest of the week's washing.
Stanhope departs, singing a gay *arioso*....

Con moto:
What a fuss about nothing How stupid can you get! I'll just go and **SHOVE** it In the Lau·au·aunderette!

Act 2 opens in a sombre *Launderama*. Unknown to *Stanhope*, the overseer is an **OGRESS**. Fearing her *terrible* ire, washer-persons cower behind their newspapers. A mood of foreboding is struck in a tense, nervous *aria*, sung by a flat-dweller, *"Oh Sheets I wouldst have folded!"*

As *Stanhope* enters, the *Ogress* rises.....

Service Wash? That's 2 pound · 50.... let's hope you're *not* feeling *thrifty!*

Boldly, *Stanhope* declines. He tries to open a washing machine.... It does not yield. He forces it. He overloads it. He over·soaps it ...chooses too hot a programme ... slams the door... rams the *wrong* money in...

Don't **RAM** it! You'll **JAM** it! **DAMN** it! I'll **KILL** you!

Oh dear! Will you?

An orchestral interlude follows, representing a tempest. A grim washer-folk chorus prays to the gods...

Help, oh help this stupid burgher!

In a brilliant *coloratura aria*, the *Ogress* re-bukes *Stanhope*....

Oh Pl·ea·se!

There follows a duet, where *Stanhope* apologises & the *Ogress*, *touched to the core*, reveals her true identity: a tender-hearted woman, turned to steel by the demands of her job.

The loads all **pong!** The hours are long! The machines go wrong! There's very little pay... ...for a 15 hour day!

At her words, the scales fall from *Stanhope's* eyes: he begins to appreciate the long hours & pongs which most women have to en-dure... including *his* wife.

O dio!

The final Act finds *Stanhope* reunited with *Trish*. He pledges a life of shared lather...

Strangers in the Night

Custom and *Infidelities* have damped down the fire in *Stanhope* and *Trish's* marriage....

"...Shannon leant forward on the sultry, jungle-print lounger, and fingered the dimmer switch with one exquisitely manicured nail. Her forms reared up at him through the fine mist of her nylon-tricot float-coat..."

But occasionally, the odd *ember* glows:

...Wild thoughts foamed in Giovanni's loins. He grasped....

What *is* it?

Just thought I'd turn out the light..Hmm?

Hold on..must finish my chapter...

What's all this then?

Ooh, I say! Dirty beast!

..this is a bit RUDE, isn't it ..eh? Eh? What're you doing reading such exciting things?

Not in the *least* exciting ...it's just some rubbish Jocasta left lying around...

It's *total* bilge...

Ah, come on! You *love* it! Don't you? Don't pretend you don't!

This!? You're joking! *Total mind-rot!*

But you can't put it down, can you?

Stanhope..look, I've had a hard day..and *this*...this sends me to sleep...it *blanks out the mind*....
..it's appallingly written..brilliantly marketed...clichéd..crapulous and totally *undemanding*...

Mmm...

But it's *sexy*, isn't it? Eh? Turns you on, doesn't it? Eh? ....eh?

No, it doesn't!

Absolutely not! Has absolutely no effect whatsoever...!

!

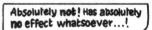

It's like cold showers...apples...long walks..absolutely the *antidote* to sex..leaves you quite cold...

Fibber!

Now..I must go to sleep..got an early start tomorrow...

Night Night

G'night

..the clingy, silk wrap. His thighs felt like steel hawsers as he c... to him. "Trish!" he "Oh Trish!" She felt melting, yielding - "Oh Giovanni!"she

..602..603.. ..604..605.. ..606...

© Posy Simmonds 1983

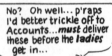

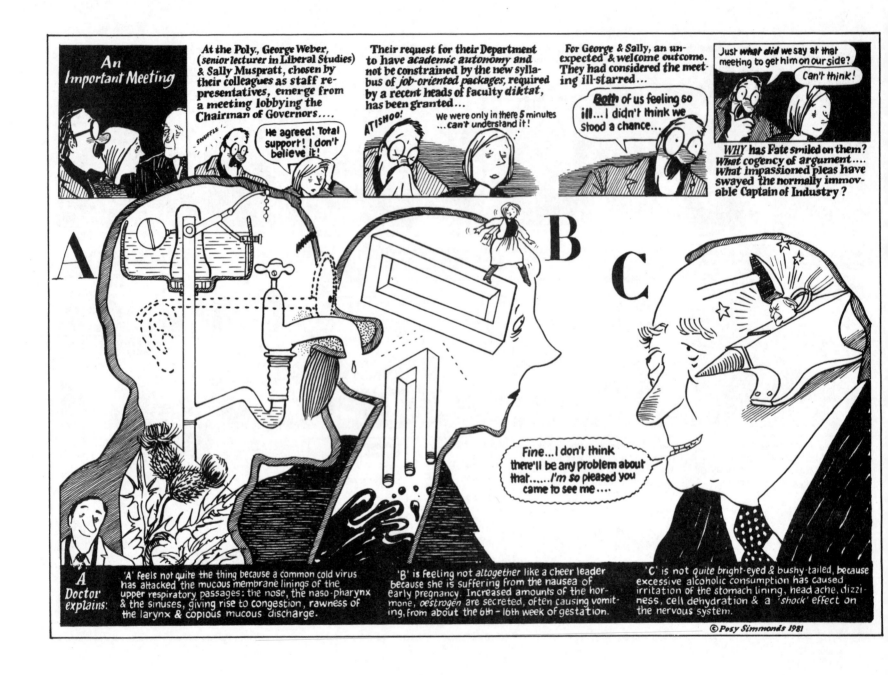

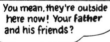

© Posy Simmonds 1983

Nature, Nurture (& Nutrition)

Belinda Weber has eschewed Further Education, in favour of a little job, helping cook for a Directors' Dining Room:

We did this really *brilliant* thing for them, today, Mum... *Coronation Chicken*... ...you get chicken breasts, right?......

...you whiz up *curry powder* in *mayonnaise*... *slosh* it on ...real *doddle*, I tell you...

RAW curry powder?

Bottle mayonnaise?

Yeh

God's truth!

..then we did this *choccy Roulade*...

...and *TOMORROW*, we're doing this cheese cake...one of the directors goes really *BARMY* over it!

That's *Alisdaire*..the one with the *SAAB*...he's really nice...he asked me for my phone number...

ANYWAY..you get all cream cheese, 'n' cream, 'n' a tin of mandarins 'n' all these ginger biccies...

sounds *QUITE* disgusting!

'Snot! They really love it!

And they *KNOW* about food!

Really?

Well, they wouldn't *touch YOUR* sort of *lentil-peasant crap*!

They like a bit of *class*!

Look.. *run away*, Belinda, would you? I've got this essay to do...the *supper* to get and the twins from Brownies...

Why you so *FOUL* to me?! *Why* you *SO bloody* about my job?!

Because it's a *silly, filling-in-time-till-marriage* job! You and your 'A' *levels*...you ought to be at *UNIVERSITY*...or training for a *proper* career!

But I don't *WANT* a *CAREER!!*

!

I wanna marry someone *RICH!* A rich company director!

I wanna *SAAB!*

I wanna have a *nice HOUSE!* I don't wanna live in a conversion in an *up & coming* neighbourhood!!

I never want a pine dresser or *roller blinds*...or *ANY*thing *PATCHWORK!!*

I *NEVER, EVER* want to eat another *lentil*... kidney bean! I'm *SICK* of brown rice!! *I wanna* eat *Cordon Bleu!* I wanna have proper dinner parties!

Oh well...if that's the way you feel....

Yeah! I *DO!*

And I'm sorry... I can't help it...

...it was the way I was brought up...

© Posy Simmonds 1983

© Posy Simmonds 1983

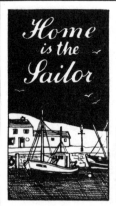

Home is the Sailor

It's lonely in Tresoddit when the fleet's away...

The little hamlet holds its breath and gazes out to sea and waits for the safe return of its wayfaring ones.....

And those remaining sons and daughters of Tresoddit, who also watch and wait, eke out a DOLEFUL existence.....

The streets are silent....

...and the hostelries; bereft of regulars...*oilskinned, seabooted, filling the bar with salty chat....*

....Only the wind howls....down the chimneys of all those depleted hearths: ..."*Crab Pots*"...."*Thrift Cottage*"...."*Everholme*"...."*Trunnions*"... .."*Ocean Spray.*"..

And then, one bright day, the first sail is spotted:

Soon, the fleet blows in to its haven....for a sojourn, which must be all too brief.

But for a short while, the streets are full of merry mariners...and all the tills ring......

One Man's Meat...

How fortunate the Webers are in having friends with country cottages. This Easter, they're staying with Pippa & Hamish. And what a comfy cottage...almost a home from home!

Delicious Camembert, Pippa...buy it locally?

God, no!

Can't get that sort of thing round **HERE**! We have to bring almost everything with us....

People here...**CAN'T** tell you what they live on!

Most part, absolute **CRAP**!

Well, I s'ppose so many of them are out of work...

Yes, they are

But you should **SEE** the sort of expensive stuff they waste their money on!

ALL convenience food! **FULL** of chemicals and **SUGAR**!

You should **SEE** their super market baskets! ...well, it's the same in **town**, as well, I've noticed ...haven't you, Wendy?

Sausages...instant **soup**... horrid, synthetic toppings.. **NOTHING** fresh! ...... I mean, if I didn't have much money, I could still eat **frightfully** well!

They don't seem to have **heard** of casseroles....

But they can only afford to **HEAT**, not **COOK**

Meat's expensive

BONES aren't!

All kinds of **wonderful BONES** you can get at the butchers... **BOIL** them up... lovely **STOCK**...

...throw in a few **odds and ends**.... whizz them up in the blender...

LOTS of lovely, lovely **SOUP**!

...or, what about **PASTA**! Costs **nothing**! If you're broke, have it like the **Italian peasants** do.... ...little **garlic**, olive oil, tiny bit of parsley... **LOVELY**!

...or.. save money on fuel, eat raw things... **crudités**... I adore crudités.... whizz up a little **aïoli**... **DELICIOUS**!

But vegetables are expensive!

Dandelions aren't!

There're **lovely** dandelions at the moment! We've eaten lots of ours in salads, recently

They're so good!

Anyway, not **ALL** veg. is expensive... What about **curly kale**? That's what people should eat...

Course, you **must** blanch it first...cook it a bit... **then** refresh it in cold water..... then re-heat it in butter.... **Delicious**! Little salt and black pepper.....

CHECK OUT

In other words, she means...

Let them eat **KALE**.

© *Posy Simmonds 1984*

Unwrappings

G.D.

The Weber Family enter a newsagents in search of ice cream for its younger members.

Accompanying them is American *ethno-botanist*, Frisbee Summers, (currently on sabbatical from the *Perceptronics Division* of a Communications Multi National.).......

O God, this'll take forever, Frisbee

I don't want a *Fruiti-frost*! You **SAID** we could have *Cornettos*! You **DID**!

No I didn't... not *today*...

Canive this, Mum?

You **SAID**!

While negotiations progress, Frisbee examines the upper shelves...

Gaad! Look at it all!! **CRAPSHEETS**!

Oh **Gaaad**!! **Sick**, George, **sick**! "lovely Josée is into scuba diving and pottery... and she's quite a *dish* too....."

Pretty *grass*, all this.. hey, George?

Oh, I don't know.. they do an efficient job as carriers of *chauvinist ideology*..

Hey, c'mon, they *mess* your *mind*, man!

But, Frisbee, you simply have to **GAPE** in admiration...

Whaat! At this **BODY CANT**!?

Yes, you can't fault them as systems of communication

Listen, can you find me a better example of *authentic polysemic image discourse*....?

Well, I know it *foregrounds* the sexual message and....

See, you have the *fur* & the *bentwood chair* lodged as *signifiers* — one, the mutually determining dynamic of *sinuosity*, which can be read as **TREE**-*limb*, get it? ...and the *fur*...well, Frisbee, the fur....

Chauvinist rhetoric, Frisbee... transparently "..the signifying aspect of the ideology...", eh?

Yeah, Right on!

...and see, here, look at this one...

Yeah, **wow**! How 'bout that, George! **AMAZING**!

It *is* interesting

Perverts!

© Posy Simmonds 1982

Monkey Business.

Some of the Weber family are visiting the Zoo. Here they are, finally, in the Monkey House....

But **what** dey doing, vose monkeys?

GRANNEE! What are they doing?

What's dat pink fing?

What is it?

Well, I can't quite..... I haven't got my right **specs**, darling...I expect it's his **tail**, don't you?

No it's not!

Yes, well, let's look at the next ones. Shall we, darlings?

But **why** do they do that?

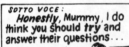

SOTTO VOCE:
Honestly, Mummy, I do think you should **try** and answer their questions...

Well, it's **SO EMBARASSING**, Wendy!

Oh **really! Tsk!** That was a **GOLDEN** opportunity just then to tell them **what is what!**

They know a **certain** amount already...

Just simple answers.... nothing **too** complicated....

I just think it's terribly important to tell them things when they ask....

And I don't want them thinking there's something **nasty & unmentionable** about **SEX**....

But they are a bit young...

Mummy, **why's** its bottom all pink?

Why is it?

Tell us!

Why is...

What is it?

What is **that?**

Tell me..

Now listen...

...sort of **signal**... blah blah ... **swelling** ... blah blah ... **girl monkeys** ...

... **courtship** ... **Daddy monkeys** ... **mating** ... blah blah ... **babies** blah blah

blah blah

© Posy Simmonds

TABOO

Here are the Weber family at Wendy's sister's, celebrating *Aunt Bunny's* 80th birthday.....

Here's Sophie...

© Posy Simmonds 1983

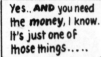

© Posy Simmonds 1983

Virtue's Work

Look, Jocasta...there **ARE** politer and *more* civilised ways of asking for **MONEY**, you know....

Tsk.. Dad!

You treat me like a *bloody* **Cash Dispenser!**

And while we're about it..this isn't a **HOTEL**...& I'm **NOT** the bloody **HALL PORTER**...

You've got perfectly good **DIGS**...why don't you live in them.....instead of lounging about here?

Told you! Can't afford it!...not on my **grant**..and what **you** give me...and there're **NO** summer jobs any more...

Jocasta..how **long's** this going on for?

I tell you...next year... when you leave college... **YOU**..have got to **wise up!**

You'll have to do a bit of **HARD WORK**...learn to be **SELF·RELIANT**.... learn the meaning of **THRIFT**, won't you, eh?

Ooh! Wonderful *virtues! Très à la mode,* Father.... very *Victorian!* ... **THRIFT! INDUSTRY!**

Yes...well...they knew a thing or two, the Victorians....Lately, I've come to think there's a lot to be said for those sort of values....

Mm..come in handy down the *dole queue*...Victorian virtues, won't they..?

Absolutely, Jocasta... absolutely...

SLOTH
A NEW VICTORIAN VIRTUE:

In these troubled times, let us praise Sloth...for, do we not perceive that, where the Spirit of Slothfulness is absent, how The Suffering Multitude FRETS & roars & clutches in vain after the coat tails of the Tyrant, WORK?

But, where Sloth dwells, then there must recline Docile Citizens, the unobtrusive recipients of National Benevolence.

The Suffering Multitude　　　*The Docile Citizen*

THE IMPORTANCE of SLOTHFULNESS:
Sloth subdues the Refractory Tendencies in Humanity, & discourages the Habit of Industry & brings to the Disorderly, the Balm of Peace.

Let us embrace Sloth! And promote that Virtue, & seek that admirable felicity of taste which finds Meaning in Enforced Idleness!

Let the sage father accustom his sons to a life of inactivity, and his daughters to bask in infinite domesticity.

For it is far better to GIVE UP and RECEIVE.

© *Posy Simmonds 1983*

We're often obliged to hang about in Life....

...But it's one of Life's *trifling* inequalities....

...that the young can at least *SIT* out an interminable wait....

....without looking out of the ordinary....

...But those of *riper* years...

(*some of whom are dying to take the weight off their feet...*)

....will risk being taken for a *serious* casualty of urban infrastructural decay....

© Posy Simmonds 1983

'S HOSPITAL'

Minor Op.

All the Ward's a Stage, And all the patients merely players: They have their exits and their entrances; And one patient in her time plays many parts:

First she plays a **WOMAN** *of forty, with a suitcase, having a minor operation....*

Your bed's this way, Mrs Weber...

Now, if you'd like to pop your nightie on ..& hop into bed...

What! actually **INTO** bed? I'm not **ill**!

...then she becomes an **INFANT**, *mewling behind a paperback.....*

SNIVEL

Now, nothing to worry about, eh?... All right, now, dear?

No..nothing to worry about....just being silly...

Then she has a small speaking rôle:

On the **Pill**? Taking any medication? — NO

Any *allergies*? *False* teeth? — NO · NO

Crowns? Did you open your bowels today? — NO · YES

Then becomes one of the Silent Watchers of the Night:

Cough · Nurse! · SCURRY

Then a **CHILD**:

..and this just relaxes you before you have your anaesthetic

GULP

Next, a larger part..that of a **DOZY FLY** *in winter.........*

WARD 9 · See you later, Mrs Weber..

...And then... **LIME-LIT** *in surgical green, she plays the part of* **LEADING LADY:**

Next, a plum rôle of **WOUNDED SOLDIER**, *returned from the front, sighing in a bower...*

Going to give Mummy her card, Benji?

..and Aunt Bunny asked after you... & the Crichleys

Ooh..there's **STAFF NURSE.. HALT!** Who goes there? *Friend* or **ENEMA!?**

HAR HAR HAR!!

Then a try for the part of **PALE HANDS** *playing on a coverlet....*

Oh well.. I think you can go home after lunch...

Really? · Oh

As soon as that?

Finally, a small walk-off part:

WAY OUT

© Posy Simmonds

At the Poly, the term progresses... the Departmental notice board is in full *leaf*.... Today, *GEORGE WEBER (Senior Lecturer in Liberal Studies)*, is struck by a recent addition......

Hey! Have you seen this?

What?

Oh, I had one in my pigeon hole...

" The attention of all members of staff is called to the decision of the school management committee at its meeting on 14 Nov. 1981, which ratified the earlier decision of the Faculty Board, to DENY access to ALL PERSONS other than APPROVED VISITORS.

The reasons for this decision are as follows:

1.i   The Education Authority is not responsible for, nor insured against, accidents which may happen to, or be occasioned by, UNAUTHORISED persons.

1.ii   Its guarantees in respect of CRIME prevention can no longer, in such circumstances, be sustained. (Instrument of Government para. 72, note iii)

2.   The unsuitability of visitors' clothing may hazardise relations to various statutes. (Staff are referred to Ray Collins for clarification on this one.)

2.i   The progress & development of the Faculty's links with local industry & commerce could be imperilled by an injudicious, apparent breach of the confidentiality implicit in such co-operative arrangements.

2.ii   The DISTRACTION produced by the presence of visitors can prejudice the academic atmosphere of application and...

What the heck is all this about?

© Posy Simmonds 1982

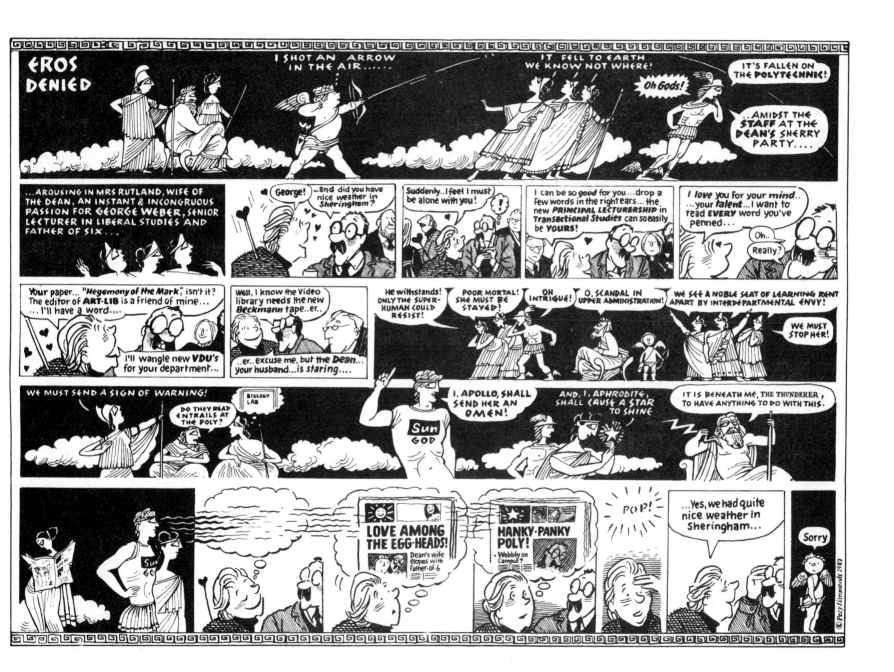

The House that JACK bought

This is the house that Jack sold.....

It's a dump but I sold it! Well.. good as sold it

This is the house that Jack wants.....

FOR SALE

This is the chap that lives in the house that Jack wants.....

Shite's the name .....

Care to see rynd?

Oh... please

This is the price asked by the chap, that lives in the house that Jack wants....

Quite a few thousand Smackeroonies, actually

God! That house!...It's perfect...perfect!

Right...we'll make him an offer.....

These are the solicitors, dressed in black.....(One for *Shite*, one for Jack).... ..who handle these things for a healthy whack......

Jack makes his offer without delay....

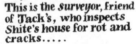

Shite's accepted!

Oh I SAY!!

...And soon the deal is under way......

This is the *surveyor*, friend of Jack's, who inspects Shite's house for rot and cracks.....

Here's Jack's contract in black and white.....*signed* by Jack, delivered to *Shite*:

...Yes, Mr Shite, he's sent it... ....AND a cheque for the deposit....

But, *this* is the *berk* who made a NEW bid...(*a few thousand more quid*)....

...That scuppered the deal and stopped the cheque...

...... causing *Shite* to crow in the morn...and tell his lawyer the *hice had gorn*....

...But we were about to exchange contracts with....!

...who rang the solicitor dressed in black:

What!?

I'm afraid my client's not going to like this!

.who passed the message on to Jack....

...it seems he had a better offer... I AM sorry....

...who *blasted* off a barrage of *flak*....

...and kicked the dog...

...and worried the cat

...and ate his hat....

...and part of a mat.....

Grrr!

Because, there they are in a short-let flat....

Paying a BOMB!

And we can't go BACK....

....to the dump of a house that Jack....

..SOLD...

© Posy Simmonds 1985

The Transports of Love

Only last month, *Stanhope's* car (*between 12·45pm & 5pm, weekdays only*), was a **Fairy Carriage**.....

"Come on.. you'll think of some excuse..."

"Mm"

...the means of escape to bosky places...

"P'raps not *too* near the Common..."

...where he gathered him rose-buds:

"This'll do"

Transport de Joie

But *this* month, his car is a **Torture Chamber**...and Stanhope has joined that *secret* society, which passes a *mauvais quart d'heure*, each evening, after the hours of business....

"Stanhope! Can I..er..um..?"

"Oh God! Oh No!"

"Look I must talk to you... *please!*"

"*Five* minutes ..please!"

"Well..you'd better get in..or someone'll see us...."

...Discreetly parked, racked and pinioned in the *crumple zone*, Stanhope endures *Brief Encounters* of sniffs and sighs and recriminations....

"..it's just that we ought not to see each other quite so often..."

"Then why did you say things if you didn't mean them..?!"

"I think Ian suspects something"

"Look..we can't go on meeting like this"

"I don't mean to hurt you ...but..."

"..Look, I really don't have time to talk about it now... I'm sorry, but I ought to be ...my wife'll be wondering..."

"You don't want to see me any more...*that it?*"

Killjoy was here....

Taxi!

Here is *Stanhope* Wright at London Airport, positively *bursting* with sap, fresh from the slopes of *St Hérisson*....

Well, I don't *have* to take 'em, guv, but I will..if you can get 'em in...

That's very *civil* of you!

Nice *TAN*... Been away?

Oh..few days skiing... just a *QUICKIE*....

Just *nipped orf*, did you?

Well... I *did* have a little business in *Geneva*...but that only took a day....

..and I had a little gap in my... *DIARY*...So I thought: *WHY NOT*? Office can look after itself...

That's the way! *ALL* for it! Got to enjoy yourself when you can, haven't you?!

Oh *YES*! I mean, *no one's* going to do it for you, are they?

No No They're not!

All *work* and no play, eh? Got to look after *Number 1*, haven't we?

Oh, we have!

Specially *these days*...no good letting things pass you by, is it?

No, no, it's not!

Not all we want, *Life*, is it?

No, it's not

But it's all we got...

True...true...

..So, we got to make the best of it

Absolutely!

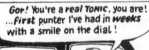

Gor! You're a *real TONIC*, you are! ...*First* punter I've had in *weeks* with a smile on the dial!

Ah...

Glad *SOMEONE's* got something to smile about...makes a change, I

Sorry?

I said...you look very *pleased* with life... *RARE* thing... what with the country up the spout...*millions* on the *breadline*...

What?

...total state of economic *collapse*... *GLOOM*... *DESPAIR*...

Look, I don't want you to think I....

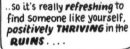

..so it's really *refreshing* to find someone like yourself, *positively THRIVING* in the *RUINS*....

Still...always a *FEW* fiddling while *Rome* burns, aren't there?...stands to reason....

It's an *ill* wind, innit?

You still there, guv?

© Posy Simmonds 1983

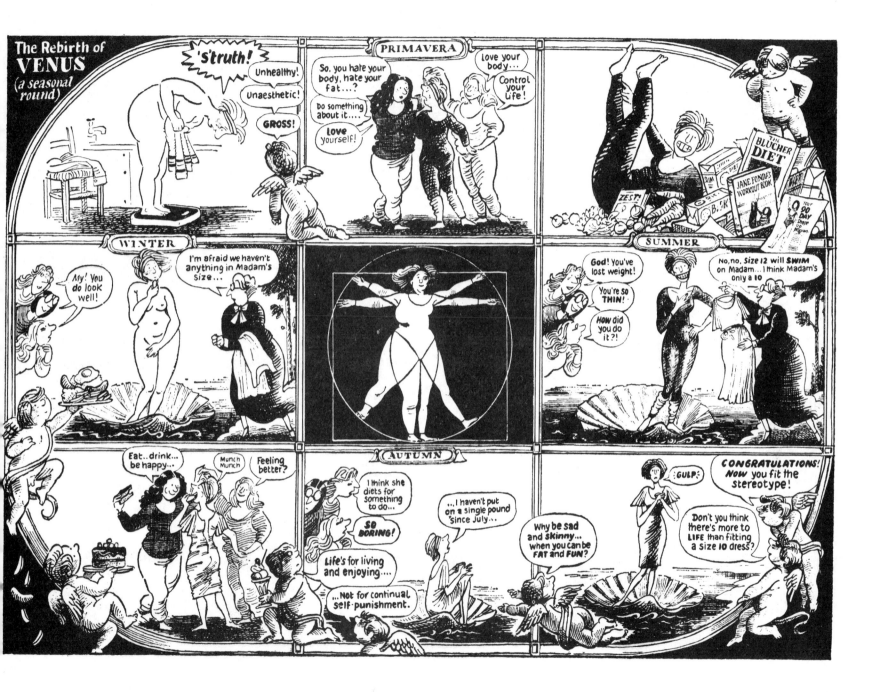

Standards of Living

It's the first time that *Benji Weber* has been left at a certain friend's house, while *Wendy* attends a lecture....

It is good of you, "Laura..

That's OK, Wendy

Later, Wendy & her mother pick Benji up...

Bye!

That *Laura's* a *sweet* thing... and *very* obliging...but.....are *you* thinking what *I'm* thinking, Wendy?

Mmn

Yes...well, I'm *afraid* I didn't find Laura's...*quite*...er... *comme il faut*.....

...**NOT ideal** for Benji, did you think?

No, not really

' Tell the truth, looking round there.... I *nearly* absolutely had **FORTY FITS!!**

I *thought* it was **GHASTLY!**

Not a place to leave a child...do you?

Well.... perhaps not

O I *AM* relieved, darling! I'm sure you'll find some one else...but I *couldn't* relax for a minute, if I knew Benji was going there again!

There were things there to **CURDLE** your blood!

Yes, there was something...

Those awful stairs! That unguarded fire! That frayed electric cord! Awful old nappies lying about! The bleach bottle! That great carving knife! Soiled tea cloths! Rucked-up rug! Cat litter all over the place...!

Yes.... that Noddy book!

© *Posy Simmonds* 1982

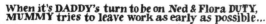

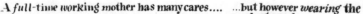

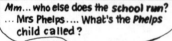

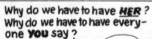

Cornish Wrestling

Here is a local taxi returning *George Weber*, his *Family Rail Card* & some of his children, to the station, after *Half Term* spent in Tresoddit....

How relaxed George feels, after his break........

...this long, carefree weekend of Discovery: *sea shells..conkers ...edible funghi..crispy leaves...*

...and *now*... a crispy *tenner*, down the side of the back seat....

Yes, as I was saying,......

Holy mackerel! £10!!

......which impales George on the horns of a dilemma:—

Psst! Finders keepers, eh, George?

SHAME! That note probably slipped out of the purse of some poor **widow woman**...visiting her sick husband in Truro hospital.....

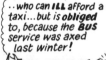

..who can **ILL** afford a taxi...but is **obliged** to, because the **BUS** service was axed last winter!

Now, hand it over to the driver....he'll ask around his clients....

Like **HELL** he will! He'll just pocket it!

He's **MORE** deserving than **YOU!**

HIM! You know who he is!?

He's a bloody **shark** from London! He's the one, moved down here... bought up all the shops round the **harbour!**

HE'S responsible for the rot in Tresoddit!

..."*Olde Lugger Fudge*"... "*Pisky Nooke*".. "*Maritime Fine Arte Ltd*"...bloody **chips** and **cowrie shells** everywhere!

..& what with his caravans, makes a bloody **KILLING** all summer, out of the tourists...and he's got the monopoly of the taxi service in the winter.....

You **CAN'T** keep it, you know!

Well, you're **not** letting that **rapacious berk** have it!!

He's **not** keeping it!

O yes he is!

He's handing it over!

No he's not!

Here we are then, squire!

That's £8·00, please...

£8·00, if you'd be so good...

Dadd-ee!

I said, £8·00, orright? Hey, you...

We'll miss the train!

Sorry! Yes..here's £10... keep the change...

Oh cheers!

Tsk!

OK..Pax!

© Posy Simmonds 1983

Mother's Quiet Time

BABA'S
Prune Yogurt
Surprise

Jocasta Wright visits an old friend,... (and new mother)...

Hi Jocasta

BWAAAAAA!!

Oh God! Not again!

What's the matter with it...I mean, *him?*

Nothing..he just *yells* all the time... ...at the clinic, they say "What *lovely* healthy lungs he's got..."

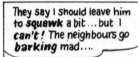

They say I should leave him to *squawk* a bit...but I *can't!* The neighbours go *barking* mad....

BWAAAAAA!!

'Praps he's got a *pin* sticking in him.

He doesn't have *pins*..he's in *disposables*...and he's not *wet*..just looked...

WAAAA AA!!

And he hasn't got *colic* or *wind*....

..he isn't *teething* or *constipated*...

And he just *spat* this lot back at me...so he's not *hungry!*

Waaa!

I've picked him up...rocked him, cuddled him, soothed him...played with him... ...tired him out...

Ssh...

I've done *everything* they say you should...

Oh God... :SIGH:

Poor you...

WAHaaAA! WAAAAAA!!

PUBLIC VIEW

Aaaaaaah!......

...Oh.... Oh dear!...... no, no, no!... not at TABLE!

Oh NO!.. in the OFFICE!.... No, no, no!

... Oh really! No!

No, no! That child's MUCH too old to be breast fed!

Oh dear... a baby with a DUMMY...

Aah... BOTTLE-FED..Jolly good second best.... (Breast is best!)

© Posy Simmonds 1984

The Milk of Human Kindness

© Posy Simmonds 1984

© Posy Simmonds 1982

© Posy Simmonds 1983

Carping at the Corner Shop

Remember when it was *Thomases'*?

And then it became *The Purple Harvest Health Shop*.....remember?

And then that *Mrs Foxe-Forester* bought it..... turned it into *"Pot, Pine & Pinny".*.......

And then the *Patels* took it over... and now it's *Supa-Martique*....

© Posy Simmonds 1985

Funeral Rights

One of George Weber's colleagues at the Poly has been killed in a car accident.

Today, George and Wendy attend her funeral in the country...

SNIFF

SNIFF

CHOKE SNIFF!

Poor George! He's so upset.....

SOB!

It's *positive PROGRESS*... a bit of *positive SEXUAL EQUALITY*... that *MEN* nowadays don't have to keep a *stiff upper lip*.... especially in *public*....

..In the *normal way*, I'm *PROUD* that George has no *inhibitions* about expressing his *GRIEF*....

...I'm *proud* he can *mourn Stella*...the only one left in the *department* who was there when George first arrived....

SNUFFLE

It's very **HEALTHY**. But in this particular instance... when there's a certain *PECKING ORDER* of *GRIEF*....

When there are others present: *husband, parents*...who have a more *legitimate* claim to *MOURN*... one must tailor one's intensity of *grief* to theirs...

SNUFFLE

...or else people will suspect something *improper* about one's relationship with the deceased!

SOB!

Who *is* that man?

Fancy *GEORGE* so upset!

..but I'd never have thought it of him & Stella

Not in a million years!

My God! You don't think...?

Who *was* that man?

No idea

A LOVER d'you think?

© *Posy Simmonds* 1981

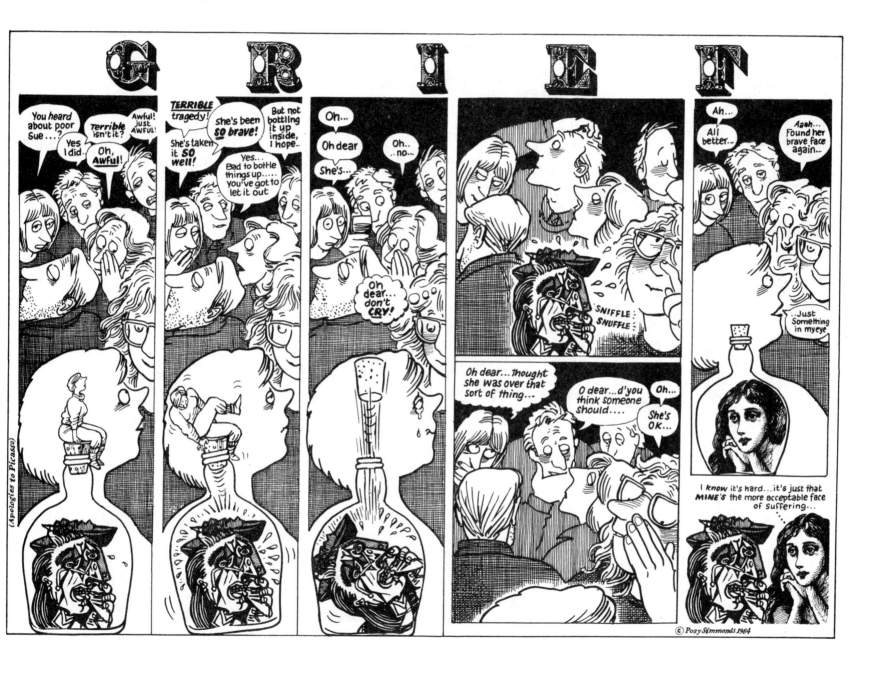

A Garden of Eden

Early September: In the mellow sunshine, *George & Wendy Weber* and their very oldest friends, turn up their toes....

TIME has faded the blossoms on the sunbeds...has eased the the tension from their rusty springs....it has relaxed the elastic of ancient beachwear...

All is peace and innocent repose...the rustle of *Sunday Supplements* and old leaves, and the gentle rise and fall of comfy waist bands.....

Gosh, Wendy... This is *PARADISE!*

Then, *Belinda Weber &* some of her friends enter the garden. .....And take a look:

LOVELY DAUGHTER GEORGE'S GOT, EH?

BUT YOU'RE STILL QUITE GOOD FOR YOUR AGE

And then all is not lovely in the garden....

...They are afraid because they are naked, and they hide themselves and cover their nakedness....

...all their *mottles & wattles* and *folds & flab* and *bunkles & bunions*....

PARADISE lost...

© Posy Simmonds 1984

Unworthy Thoughts

Twice a month, these days, the children stay Saturday night & Sunday with their father....

Mummee! We're back!

And did you have a lovely time?

Yeah.

THINKS: *I'll* bet! He never makes *ANY* effort with them... *never* takes them anywhere!

Lots of video games and pin-ball?

Left them down the *Amusement Arcade*.. ..or in the *pub* garden, as usual......

No, we didn't

What, *no* Space Invaders?!

God! He's *lazy!* Didn't take them out *AT ALL !!*

No! Daddy took us on a *MARCH*... wiv fousands of people!

Oh! The *MARCH! Damn!!* Clean forgot about it..... *Damn!* I wanted to go!

It's to stop people dropping bombs everywhere....

...and to stop *WARS*...

..so *we* can grow up...

...and not have *rayjo active* babies...

Good to know he's concerned about something again...*I just* don't believe it.....

Did *Dad* know lots of people on the march?

NO..

Oh....

...only Suzy...

Suzy? That a friend of his?

Tsk! What's he picked up, now..?

Yes, we went with her.. she's very *NICE* .. she's a nurse...

Oh...

We had *lovely* hamburgers, Mum

'Thought you didn't *like* them

Tsk! Off a *stand* as usual! *Why* does he have to feed them *JUNK !?*

No! Daddy *MADE* these ones! *And* baked potatoes!

Oh...

He said he couldn't take us out to eat 'cos he didn't have enough money...

Didn't have enough money... *my FOOT!* Mean sod!

...'cos he bought us *new* shoes.... *AND* E·T· lunch boxes!

Lemmee show you!

Oooorh!!

And *Suzy* read us lots 'n' lots of bedtime stawies!

How lovely

So *Suzy* came back, did she? But, *no,* she *didn't* stay the night... did she? *Not* in front of the *children*..nooo! Because *I'd* get to hear of it, *wouldn't* I?

And did *Suzy* read *Daddy* a story?

No! She had to go on *NIGHT DUTY*

Oh yes, she *would,* wouldn't she?

Can we watch telly?

Yes, darling.

Right! Well, *that* does it... Hasn't put a *foot* wrong all weekend, *has* he?..new shoes ...homemade hamburgers.... sensitive girl friends!!......

Michael! *What're* you doing? *Why're* you trying to get on the right side of me!? *What* are you *up* to?!! *Why're* you *SUCKING UP!!?* Why're you such a hypocrit! Why're y... .. !!! !!! !!

© Posy Simmonds 1983

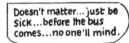

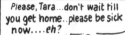

© Posy Simmonds 1983

Cat Lovers

The cat sat on the mat.

Back to the flat, come Pat and Jack.

Jack *hates* the cat.

The cat *hates* Jack.

Pat loves the cat.

The cat loves Pat.

Pat sat on Jack's lap.

Jack pets Pat.

Jack and Pat want a nap.

Scram, cat, scram!

Drat the cat!

Julian & Jolly Heep are having a night out at the cinema.....

It is an evening *fraught* with incident and *danger*.....

...an evening of swift retreats....

It is an evening of much *scampering* in the auditorium....

...of *enraged* cinema personnel...

...of escape...and near duffings-up...

But the *worst* ordeal lies ahead: The Parental Inquisition......

...See, this professor *dude*, Gabilsky, or some-ink...he's *MAD* an' it's *googol plex years* in the future an' he's planned the destruction of the world...an' he escapes in this sort of *time-dilation-effect* machine...an' it's really *SICK* cos' everything putrifies, wasn't it, Jolly? All them yellow *maggots Eeuuch!* An' this dude escapes but there're these other dudes in a space ship, chasing him. An' this dude is *bizzing 'imself*, not the professor dude, but another dude an' they run into this great *particle storm*, wiv all muons an' hadrons buzzin' about an' he blacks out with too many g's...*not* the other dude, but the professor dude...an' then he *sees* this other dude...

© *Posy Simmonds 1981*

© Posy Simmonds 1983

Every Picture...

Deep in the country, the cuckoo calls: *C natural, G sharp...*

...and in their *second home*, the Wrights (& their guests), nestle briefly, over the Bank Holiday.

Oh, what a SHAME, your veggy garden, Trish!

Yet, I must've put down a MILLION slug pellets at Easter...

Here, sunbeams *irradiate* & turn to *gold* a tranquil moment: Brunch *en plein air.*

All this, Jocasta captures...

...her *father's* look of calm repose, as he deliberates the *right* moment to nip down to the phone box near the pub and ring his girl friend....

Hey...Dad!

...her stepmother's ruminative guise, as she wonders *how* she can *possibly* be six days overdue....

Couldn't have been that time after the Lawsons' party...surely!?

Hey... Trish!

...her grandmother's serenity as she reflects on an awful night in a damp bed...

Dis one, Ganny! Smehwull dis one! See woo like budder! Dis one! DIS ONE! Dis one! Dis one!

...her tiny half-brother's air of anticipation...

Willy! Granny!

Smehwull dis One!!

....the relaxed manner of her parents' guests ...as Paul curses his host's *stinginess* with the booze and wonders if the pub'll cash him a cheque...

Hey... Paul!

THE GUA

Missile probe

...& Laura frets that the *whole* house must have heard *everything* last night, as it was only when Stanhope coughed next door, that she & Paul realised the walls were only the *flimsiest* partitions...

Hey...Laura!

Have you got cellulite jodhpurs?

ALL these precious, golden moments, Jocasta captures:

HOME

♪ 'Mid pleasures and palaces, ...though we may roam......

Can you lend us couple of quid, Liz?

Sorry, Jocasta... ...Skint, too...

♪ Be it ever so humble........ ..there's no place like Home......

Hallo Dad! ...Trish!

Why...Jocasta!

Alright if I come home for a bit?

HOW NICE!

See, 'thought I'd live at home a bit and save some money....See, I just can't afford DIGS on my grant ...and what you give me...

Well, of course, you're very welcome...

..Well, of course..she's very welcome!

YES, Mother, YES... she's very welcome ...made herself QUITE at home.... especially with the drinks cupboard...

♪ Home......Home.....

Of course she's very welcome...but, you know, she does DAMN all in the house, except EAT & SLEEP...and SMOKE! Occasionally she slopes into college....

'Course, it IS so tricky for them these days... finding some where else to live....

Stanhope...look, she's very welcome, but I'm afraid she'll never leave... They DON'T leave home, these days! Look at the Grant boy...25 and still at home! And those Carr children...both over 21.... And the Owens...their son's 28!

Jocasta..of course you're very welcome here...but I think we WOULD like to know your plans.....

Don't you think it's... about time you....

HOME SWEET HOME

© Posy Simmonds

Lady Bountiful

Here is *Wendy Weber* and a friend returning from a trip to Sainsbury's...

You **smile** a lot at people, Wendy, don't you?

Mm..suppose I do...

Yes..I do smile at people...

I *noticed!*...those teenagers back there..that old woman ...the Pakistani lady...that **vicar**...why'd you smile at him?

Oh I always do...I mean...we ..don't go to church...but *George* likes to beard him about *Synod politics*.....and he does *such* a lot of good round here....

...and I smile at the *Sweeper*, because it's such a bloody awful job....

...and **old ladies**....because, well.... *I'd* like to be *Smiled* at when I'm old...

...and at the kids on the corner...because it's so awful for them being out of work...and I think, that might be my kids soon....

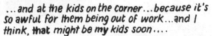

...and at the Pakistani lady because she's only just moved to this road...and people are a bit *po-faced*.......

God! You smile at **EVERYONE!**

..but I often wonder why *they* smile at **ME**...

No! Not everyone!.....I don't *smile* at those **Haymer-Smythes**, opposite..*he's* such a *racist thug!*...well, so is *she*!

I *see!*...so...it's only the poor and the meek...

...the *socially handicapped*...people you feel *sorry* for, who get smiles..eh?

Really Wendy!

Oh...

© Posy Simmonds 1983

The Sausage Roll that changed The World: *(a little)*

This is the sausage roll in question.... one of a batch prepared by the fair hand of the Dean's son...

(wodges of sausage, flaky pastry brushed with egg, left over-long in a hot oven.)

This is the fateful occasion: Each September at the Polytechnic, the Dean interrupts the remains of the vacation, in order that he and Mrs Rutland, may bid a premature *"Salvete!"* to the members of his faculty, over sherry and titbits, following a brief staff meeting...

Bloody waste of time, this is...

Just to prove we're lackeys....

The weather was LOVELY the first week... then it bucketed!

..er, Dean, there WAS one thing.. ..er, I was HOPING to hear something FIRM about the part-timers' contracts... er....

Not NOW, George ...here, let me press you to a cheese puff!

But *George Weber* has *NO* time for cheese puffs. He is *very* concerned that the *cut-backs* in part-timers will *ruin* his new course on the culture of *Turn-of-the-Century-Vienna......*

But, Dean! They're CRUCIAL, these part-timers... we NEED them!

Your department has used rather a large quota of the part-time hours, Weber...

MUNCH MUNCH

I say! These cheesey jobs are rather good!

See, Rowbotham's doing drama.. Schnitzler, Hofmannsthal, Trakl.. ...and he's producing Kokoschka's play, with 2nd Year Industrial Design....

GULP MUNCH

Mm.

...Dick Perch is doing..er.. the design history...er.. Moser, Roller and Löffler.. ..& the music: Shoenberg, of course.....

MUNCH Ye-es MUNCH

And *Ron Clarke's* absolutely essential for the psychology programme...

MUNCH MUNCH

Ooh... Sausage rolls!

...Myself,... I can deal with the Post-Nietzscheans....

GOLLOP GULP

And then the sausage roll strikes..

GLAAH

The Dean is rendered speechless......a wodge of sausage-meat blocks his windpipe...

God! Was it something I said?

?

In just four minutes, the Dean could *expire!* How fortunate it is that George's wife, (an ex-nurse), is acquainted with the *Dr Henry Heimlich Manoeuvre for Chokers:*

QUICK! Let me at him!

Grasping the Dean from behind, she *thrusts* her fist upwards into his abdomen:

The offending gristle is expelled....

...and within minutes, the Dean is himself again:

Dear me!

She saved my life, your wife did....

How lucky you brought her, tonight!

Well... let me see, now... I think we'll have to see what can be done with some of the PROBLEMS of your course... and perhaps I can bend the ear of the Chief Education Officer about the expenses of your essential trip to Venice... let's see... what else?...

!

It's an ill windpipe... ....

This is the current bivouac catalogue:

It is filled with *100's of exciting ideas* in contemporary *home-styling.*

This is the *couldn't-be-easier* mail order form:

These are the six bivouac stores...... where shopping is a *pleasure-thing*....

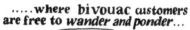

.....where bivouac customers are free to *wander and ponder*...

Ooh! These lamps are nice!

...to muse 'n' choose... ...to pay 'n' take away .....

I think I like those!

Yes!

Nice!

This is rather.

I think we need **TWO**... don't you think, George?

That's £59·90 please.

You're welcome!

These are some typical customers, beaming from their bivouac experience, leaving the *store* with that special *can't-wait-to-get-it-home-&-use-it* feeling!

Thank you.

Here they are outside the store with that special *can't-wait-to-get-it-home-&-use-it* feeling wearing off....

We don't need **2** Wendy...

I mean I didn't like to say anything in front of... too late, anyway... So *extravagant!*

And I thought we'd agreed to *draw in our horns* a bit, financially....?

Why *is it* you always jump on me when I buy something?

I don't

Yes you do!

And here are the bivouac customers with that *can't-wait-to-get-home-&-have-a-really-good-row* feeling....

And I know what it's about, George... deep down, you feel **our** money's **YOURS!** 'Cos you **earned** it....

..and I know I'm just a housewife

And here are two exciting bivouac designs in their final resting place....

© *Posy Simmonds 1981*

Nice Little Men

It's *quite a worry*, one's country cottage, this polar weather...one *has* to drive out there and check the pipes haven't done anything ghastly.....

Oh God!

But *Help* is soon summoned:

Oh, You *ANGEL!!* How *sweet* of you to come so quickly!!!

It's the *LOO!*

Oh, ar?

And Help is soon diligently going about its business....

No... Toilet don't fill up, does he? ...Well, better check your sink...and all the pipe runs.....

Super!

Oh, the WATER TANK's fine, actually... got *tons* of 8 inch quilting insulation up there...you know...between the joists.....

Have a look, shall I?....

Hallo? Your TANK's solid ICE...my club hammer don't even CRACK it... See, you've got no lagging..

Oh Nayoh!

Oh GOD!

Diligently...diligently he works.....

♪ Ai..Ai...De-li-lah! ♫
♪ Ai...Ai...De-li-lah ♫♪

Now what to do...

Hm

Long job...take day or two with hair-dryers, melting *THAT!* Draughty old place, like this...

...until, beneath him, he hears the lady's voice, telephoning her husband....

♪ Tie a yellow ribbon round the old oak tree ♫♪ ♪

Hello darling... ...yes.... ...bad news ...the tank ...yes... absolutely SOLID...

eh?

..But SUCH a nice little man's come.....Yes! Yes, almost immediately! So sweet!

!

Yes..he's so thorough! ...looked *everywhere* ...linen cupboard... ...but SO TIDY! He put everything back so TWEELY!

No! You wouldn't get that sort of service in town! You'd just get some frightful COWBOY.....yes! All spaghetti pipe-work!

No...he's a real POPPET! Absolute Salt of the Earth... you know the type...

Salt of the Earth! I'll give urr Salt of the Earth, I will!

Just going to make him a nice CUPPA...got no milk ...hope he doesn't mind POWDERED.... What? Sugar? Oh yes, I'll put lots of sugar in..they always take sugar, don't they! Yes...he's SUCH a NICE little man..

Rude BAGGAGE! Poppet! I'll give urr poppet! She can have COWBOYS, she can!!

And the angry plumber turns from the greater toil:.....and commits an act of lightning pipe-work in the downstairs loo....

There! The water's feeding straight into the cistern, now....

But I thought you said this would take days to mend?

No..well, this'll do nicely...time being... ...till it thaws... and then you can ring me again...

Darling? Yes...sorry to bother you, again ...but he's GONE.....yes...just shoved off...seemed in *rather a BATE*....well, he *has* done something, sort of *pro tem*. ...but he didn't clear up...POOLS of water on the floor....

Funny, isn't it? He seemed such a NICE little man, too...

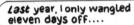

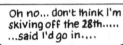

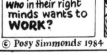

© Posy Simmonds 1984

Christmas PRESENT

Aunty Bunny's seasonal tributes are received with *ANGUISH*....

A *Stagecoach!!* Aaareugch!

Oh George! *Poor* Aunty Bunny! It's only a *CARD!*

...*not one* I'd choose, myself, but...

Yes...it's only a card, wishing the family all the Joy of *An Olde-Fashioned Xmas*.. ...and a handsome Fruit cake, baked according to *Mrs Trivet's* ancient recipe, for the *Edwardian Nobility*.....

What's the *MATTER* with it? I mean... the shops are *full* of stuff like that...

YES! Rubbish got up in *Victorian* packaging!

Have you *looked* at this cake tin, Wendy? It's just *PASTICHE!*

Half the ingredients're *SYNTHETIC*....But! Dress the thing up in *Victoriana*, and you give it *QUALITY*...

...*TRADITION*...*INTEGRITY*... *CLASS* — The Poor Man at his gate... ...what the *ADS* call "a vanished way of life"...*Remaking* the *PAST* in *SUGAR*....

That's what *Christmas* has become: A bogus pastiche of a *Fantasy Past*.....

It makes me *SICK*, Wendy!...This *Looking-Back DISEASE*...it's *every-where!* ....clutching at a *PAST* for reassurance...this *fantasy* of a Victorian *Never-Never Land!* This total lack of confidence in the *FUTURE!* The inability to look forward!

Well, I don't blame people...

Everywhere, I'm wished an *Olde Fashioned Christmas!* What *I'd* like, is a thoroughly *MODERN*, out and out *FORWARD-LOOKING* one....

I can't imagine it...

Well... *NO stagecoaches*, for a start....

Oh

And *no* jolly, Dickensian coves, sipping port... ..or *crinolines*...or *lanterns*...or *holly*... or *ivy*...or *pheasants*...*No snowmen*.... and definitely *NO robins!*

And *OUT* with *Santa*....in fact, *out* with everything, except a message of *Peace & Goodwill*, to face the Future

So...er.. Peace and Goodwill.....

Cold!

And all that remains in the wintry waste, is Peace and Goodwill....and the Chill Breath of the Future *gusts* across the plain...and, on it, the sound of *Something Hungry*, howling beyond the horizon..... *shivering* the very cones of the sentinel pines.....

Cold!

Brrrr!

Cold!

George..? The *Yule Log*... you forgot the Yule Log... *OUT* with that, too?

Keep the Yule Log.... I'm feeling the chill....

Frightfully late, one Christmas Eve....

© Posy Simmonds 1983

A MESSAGE TO
The MONSTROUS Regiment

FROM: Field Marshal Sir Desmond Blundel-Bolass, and the Massed Captains of Industry, and Chiefs of the Market Forces.

Now, look here...

...It has come to my attention, that there is **LOW MORALE** and an *appalling* Lack of *Discipline & Esprit de Corps* amongst you **WOMEN** of the *Monstrous Regiment*...

HEAR HEAR

This is **FRIGHTFUL!**

The **Monstrous** is a **FINE** little regiment, whose scrolls...if not exactly charged with **HONOURS**, nevertheless, bear a really **VERY CREDITABLE** record of **CATERING** and **CHILDCARE**...

You should **ALL** be proud to belong!

(Regimental Insignia of the Monstrous)

UBIQUE
SUBSERVIO

But, **NOW**...what grieves me *unutterably*, is that *certain* **BOLSHIE ELEMENTS** among you, have got hold of a lot of **TOM FOOL** ideas.

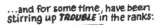

...and for some time, have been stirring up **TROUBLE** in the ranks:

EQUALITY NOW!

...There's been a lot of coat-trailing ...**dereliction** of *domestic* duties ....women going **A.W.O.L.**.... ..that kind of *caper*....

You look after him...I'm going out.

Furthermore, many of you have been trying to get yourselves **TRANSFERRED** to the **CRACK** regiments: Industry, ...*Business*... Stock Exchange...and so forth...

Shame!

It's *simply* **NOT ON!** We can't **ALL** be up the **SHARP END!** ...do I make myself clear?

Hear! Hear!

Bloody women flooding the JOB market

Point One: The duties of the **Monstrous** Regiment, **MODEST** though they may be, ...are **VITAL** to the smooth running of the *whole show*....

I want you women to return to your units and carry out your duties, as laid down.....

...otherwise, **COMPLETE SHAMBLES!**

Point Two: I've got some **GOOD** news for you... we're stepping up on *new equipment*. There will be constant *new* issues of **CATERING** *matériel* and **UNIFORMS**, from our factories, supported by **propaganda**, to keep you on your toes.....

Women & Hearth
New Dream Kitchens!
Fashion

...and we've been assured of a constant supply of **TRAINING MANUALS**.....

Heartsease Kara Pleshette
Windspill Denise Jobell

Now, do **BRACE UP!** Do I make myself clear?

© Posy Simmonds 1984